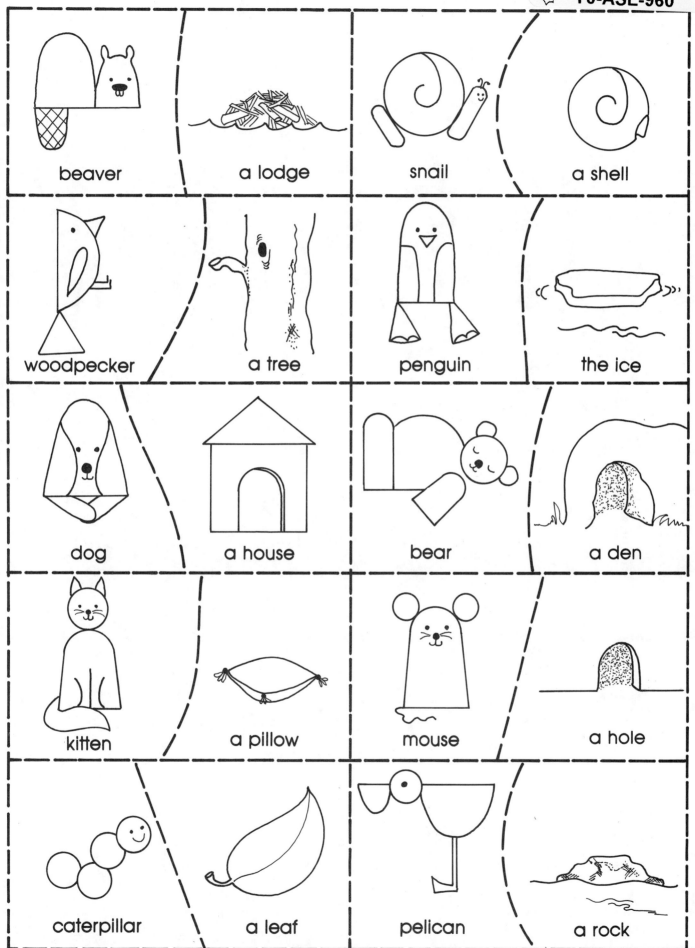

beaver — a lodge

snail — a shell

woodpecker — a tree

penguin — the ice

dog — a house

bear — a den

kitten — a pillow

mouse — a hole

caterpillar — a leaf

pelican — a rock

crocodile

a swamp

hippo

the zoo

whale

the sea

duck

a pond

pig

a sty

bunny

a burrow

turtle

a shell

frog

a lily-pond

hen

a nest

bee

a hive

Animal Homes

Turtle's Home

Turtle's home is a shell.
It fits him very well.

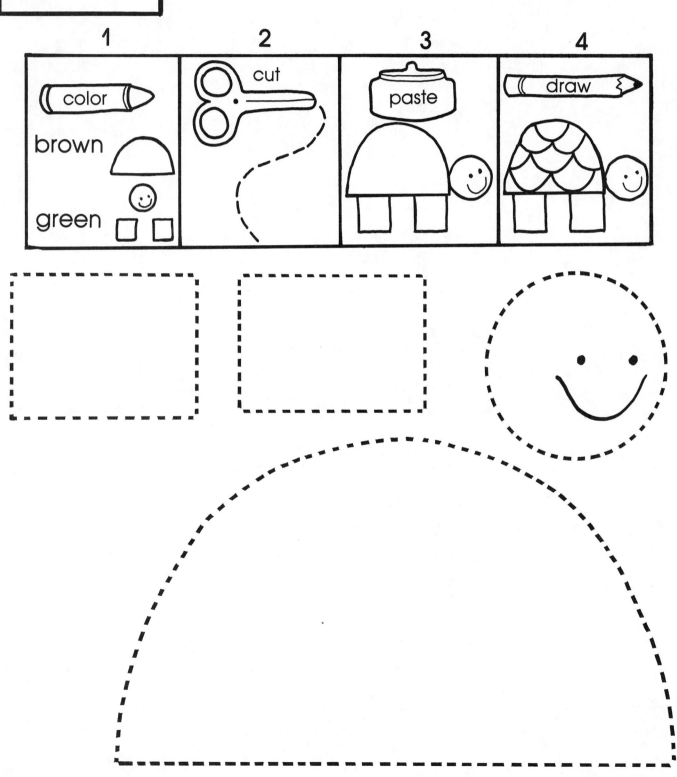

Duck's Home

Yellow duck is very fond
Of her home by the pond.

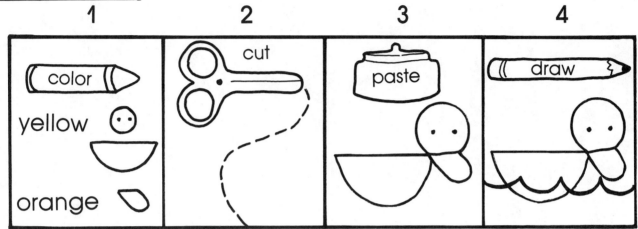

1   color yellow orange

2   cut

3   paste

4   draw

Snail's Home

Carrying her home upon her back
Snail moves along a shiny track.

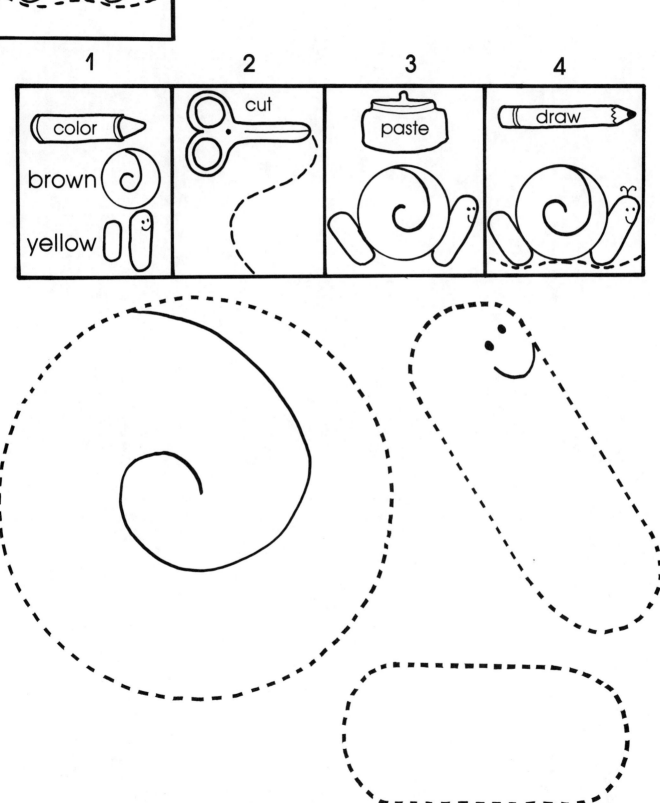

1   2   3   4

color
brown
yellow

cut

paste

draw

Hippo's Home

Hippo's home is in the zoo.
You watch him. He watches you.

1   **2**   **3**   **4**

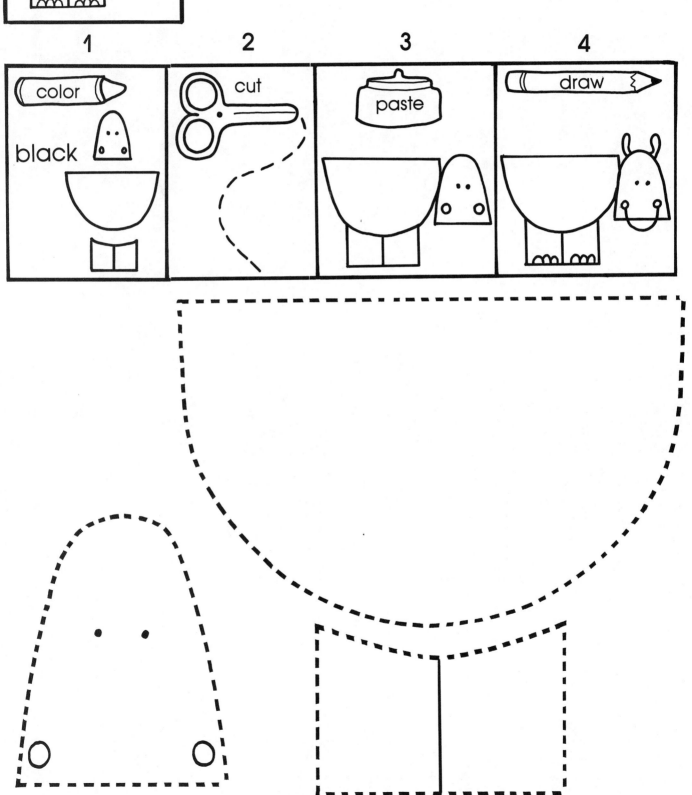

color

black

cut

paste

draw

6   Animal Homes

Kitten's Home

When little kitten wants to rest
A fluffy pillow, she likes best.

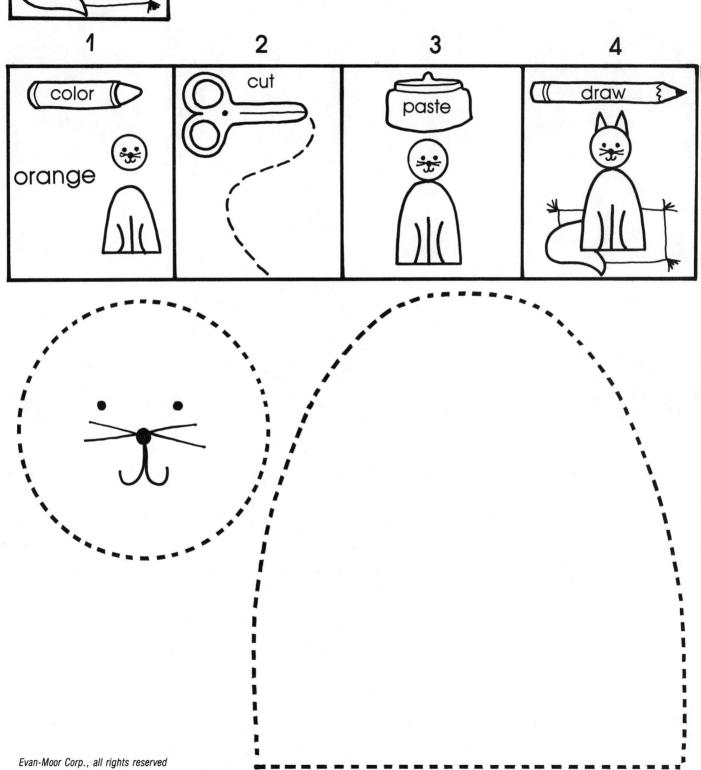

1 color orange

2 cut

3 paste

4 draw

Animal Homes

Mouse's Home

A hole is the house
For this tiny mouse.

1	2	3	4
color black red	cut	paste	draw

Dog's Home

I built a little house of wood
For my dog who is very good.

1   **2**   **3**   **4**

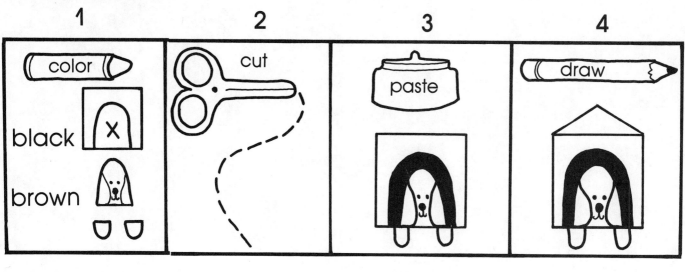

color

black

brown

cut

paste

draw

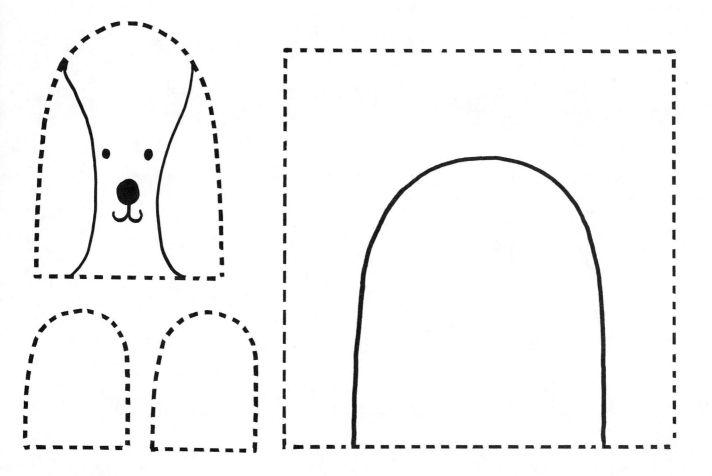

Woodpecker's Home

Woodpecker rests on a tree or pole.
He stores his food inside a hole.

1   **2**   **3**   **4**

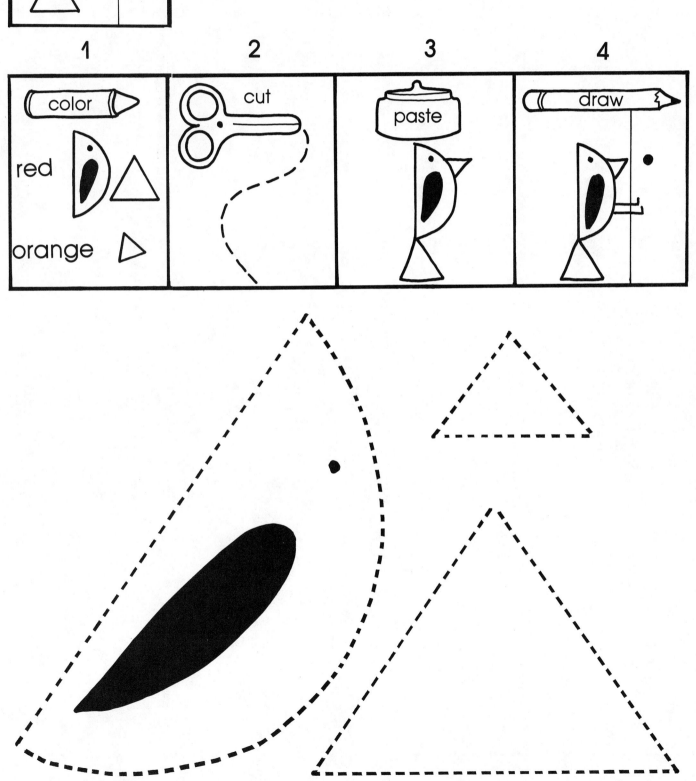

color

red

orange

cut

paste

draw

Animal Homes

Bear's Home

Bear's home in winter is a den
In springtime he goes out again!

1   color brown

2   cut

3   paste

4   draw

Bunny's Home

Furry bunny can be found
In a burrow underground.

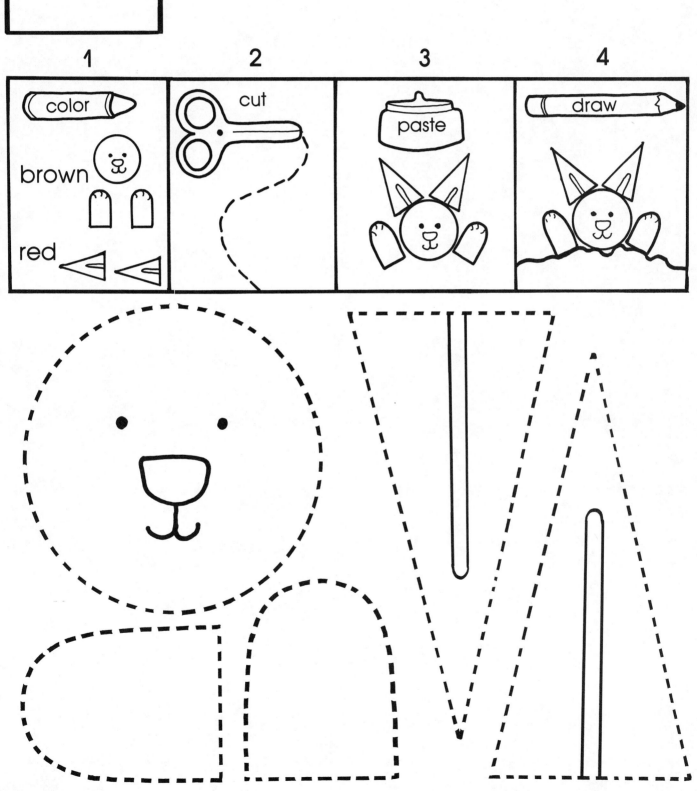

1   2   3   4

color

brown

red

cut

paste

draw

Animal Homes

Whale's Home

No matter how big a whale gets to be
He can always find room for a home in
the sea!

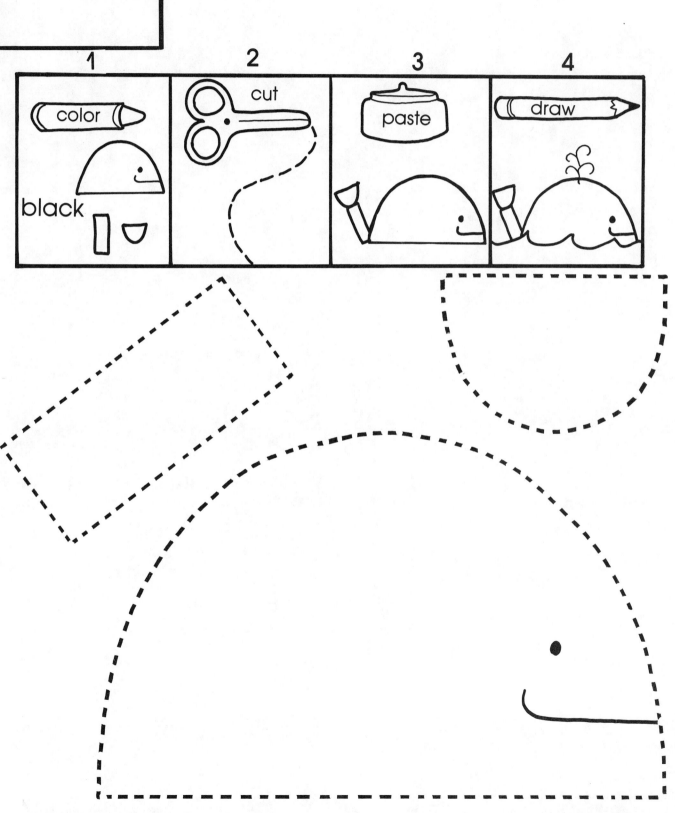

1
color
black

2
cut

3
paste

4
draw

13

Animal Homes

Caterpillar's Home

A tasty leaf, tender and green,
Is where caterpillar will be seen.

Penguin's Home

This penguin finds it very nice
To have a home upon the ice.

1 color

black

orange

2 cut

3 paste

4 draw

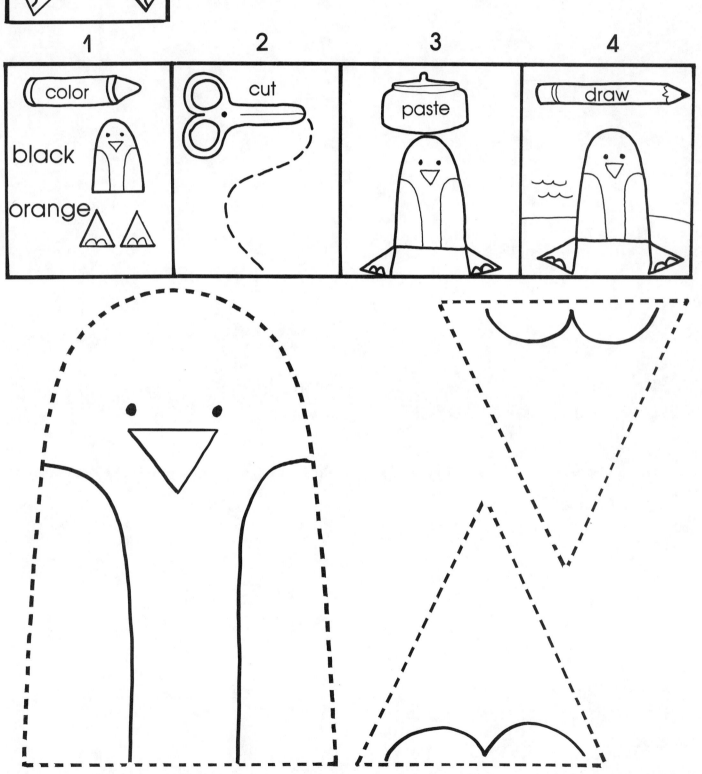

Hen's Home

When she is ready for a rest
Mother hen sits on her nest.

1   **2**   **3**   **4**

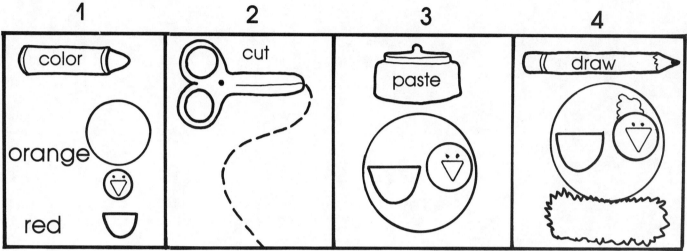

1 color — orange, red
2 cut
3 paste
4 draw

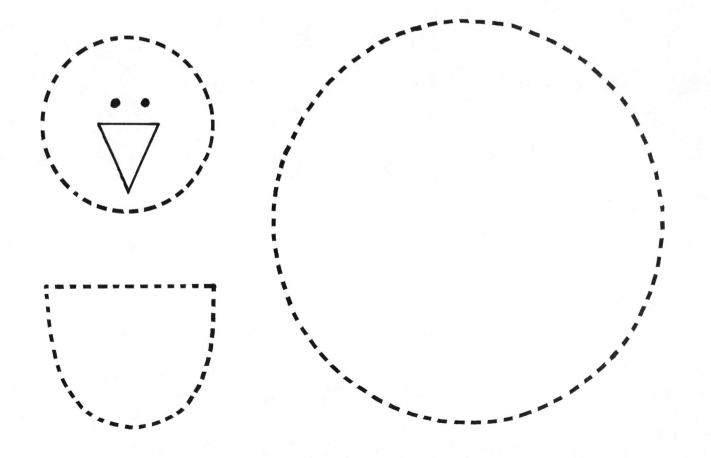

16   Animal Homes

Pelican's Home

Pelican makes a noisy squawk
As he rests upon a rock.

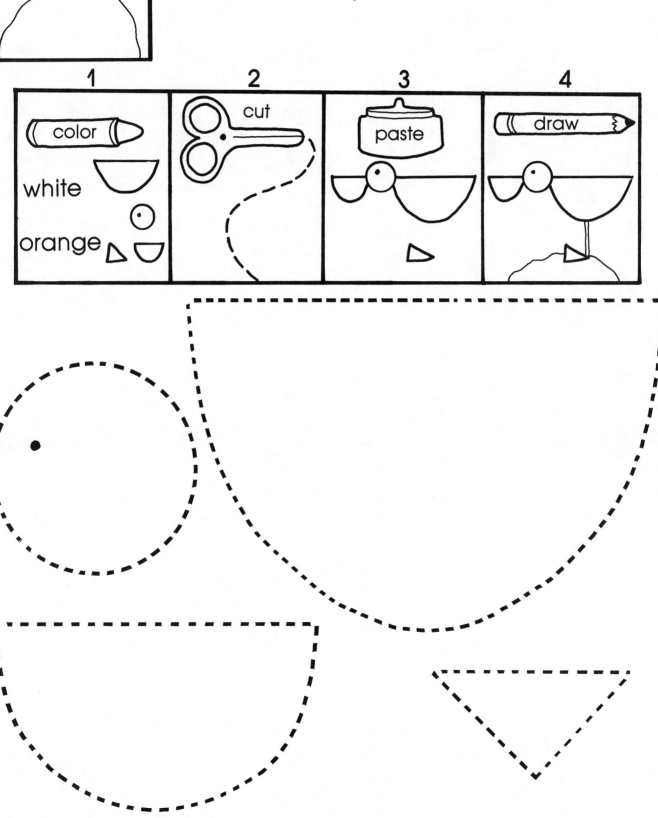

1 — color — white — orange

2 — cut

3 — paste

4 — draw

Beaver's Home

A lodge of mud and sticks together
Is beaver's home in all kinds of weather.

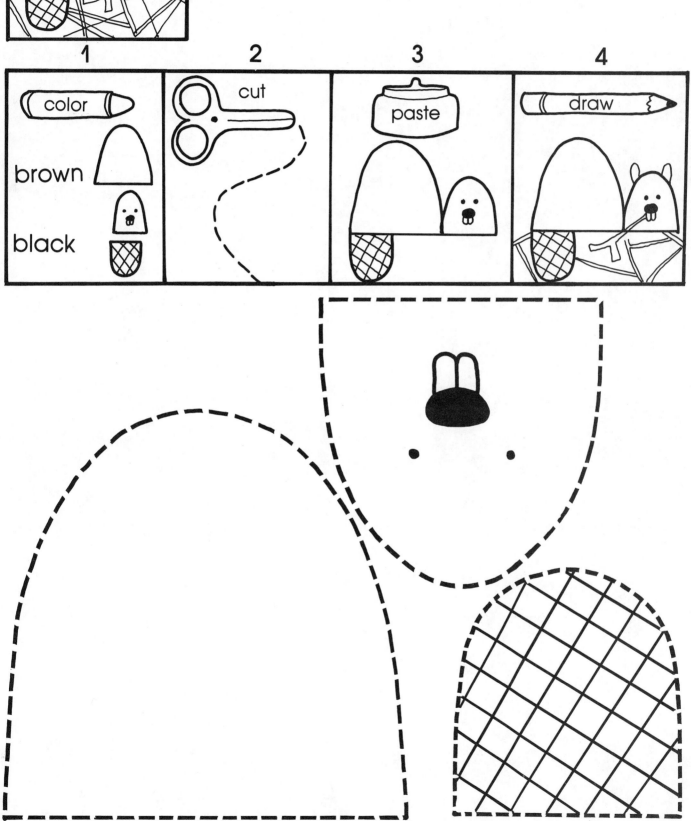

1

color

brown

black

2

cut

3

paste

4

draw

Pig's Home

I don't know the reason why
But a pig's home is called a sty.

| 1 | 2 | 3 | 4 |

Frog's Home

Green frog is very glad
To have a home on a lily-pad.

1   **2**   **3**   **4**

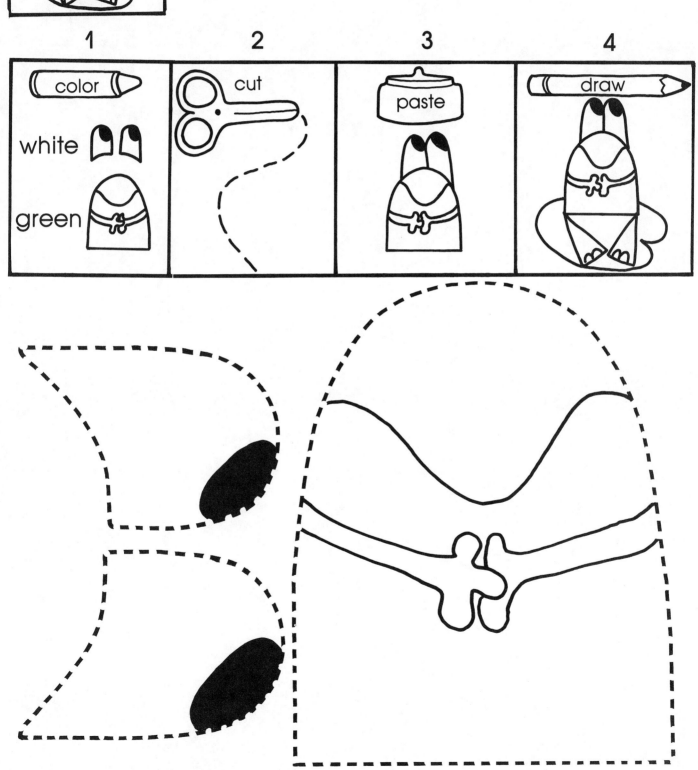

color

white

green

cut

paste

draw

20

Animal Homes

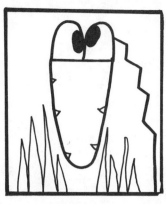

Crocodile's Home

Sharp-toothed crocodiles stay
In a swamp most of the day.

1	2	3	4

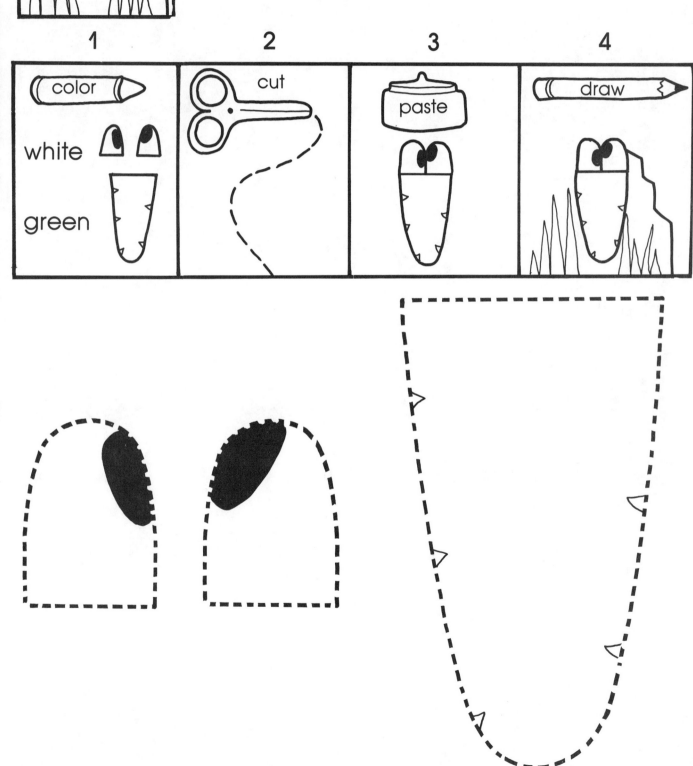

Honey Bee's Home

Busy bee flies round and round
Then goes to his hive with the pollen
he's found.

1   **2**   **3**   **4**

color
black
yellow

cut

paste

draw

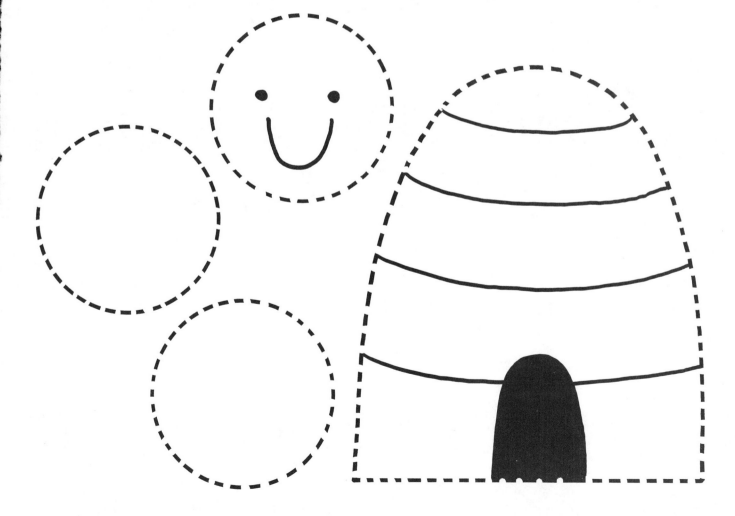

22   Animal Homes